Arkas, *Flying Starts*
*HONOR THY FATHER...*

Arkas 1993, Greece
Translation: Ingrid Behrmann

Distribution:
7, Gravias Str., 106 78 Athens, Greece
210.38.07.689 - fax: 210.38.10.892
w w w . p r o t o p o r i a . g r
www.arkas.gr

# Flying STARTS

## by Arkas

Translation
INGRID BEHRMANN

*grammata*

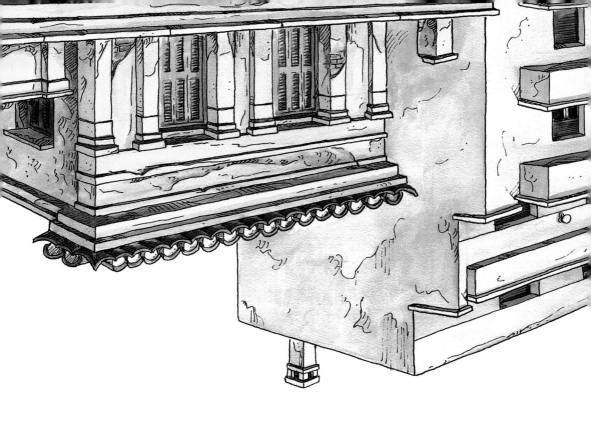

# HONOR THY FATHER...

by Arkas

LET'S SIT DOWN HERE A BIT WITH THE OTHER BIRDS!

FLAP FLAP

WHAT'S WRONG? WHY ARE THEY LEAVING?

THEY SAW THE KID!..

...I'M SURE YOU KNOW YOUR SON IS NOT VERY POPULAR...

YES, BUT FOR ALL THE BIRDS TO FLY AWAY AS SOON AS THEY SEE HIM?!

EXACTLY!.. HE COULD MAKE A LIVING AS A SCARECROW!

Αρκάς

©ΑΡΚΑΣ

WITH YOUR DISGUSTING BEHAVIOR YOU'VE GOT EVERYONE TO DISLIKE YOU!.. NOW, ARE YOU HAPPY WITH THAT?

GET LOST!

WHAT DO YOU MEAN, "GET LOST"?.. WHY DON'T YOU LISTEN WHEN I'M TALKING TO YOU? WHY CAN'T WE DISCUSS QUIETLY JUST ONCE LIKE FATHER AND SON?

OKAY! WHO'LL BE THE FATHER?

YOU THINK YOU'RE VERY CLEVER, DON'T YOU? WELL YOU'RE NOT! YOU DON'T KNOW EVERYTHING IN LIFE AND YOU MUST LISTEN TO US GROWN-UPS!..

WHY?

BECAUSE YOU MUST TRY TO LEARN FROM LIFE!

I'M TRYING, BUT LIFE'S NOT CO-OPERATING!

·Arkas

©ΑΡΚΑΣ.

11

AH!.. WHAT A DARLING!..

YOU'RE A SWEET LITTLE THING, YOU KNOW!..

YOU'RE THE MOST CHARMING, SWEET AND DEAR LITTLE KID I'VE EVER SEEN!..

WHO, ME?

YES, YOU!.. COME HERE AND I'LL GIVE YOU A HUG!

NOW, EITHER YOU'RE A CHILD ABUSER OR YOU'RE A STRANGER TO THESE PARTS!

Άρκάς

WHERE'VE YOU BEEN? WHY ARE YOU LATE?

I WAS TALKING TO A GENTLEMAN.

WHAT GENTLEMAN?

THE ONE IN THE PARK OVER THERE WHO GAVE ME CANDIES AND THEN STARTED CHATTING ME UP!

OH MY GOD!

HAVEN'T I ALWAYS TOLD YOU NEVER TO SPEAK TO STRANGERS?

WHY NOT?

BECAUSE THEN THEY'LL SUE ME!

@APKA2

'ApKas

THE FOOD IS ONLY FOR MY OWN CHILDREN!

WHAT?!

THEN WHY DON'T YOU PUT UP A SIGN SO PEOPLE DON'T WASTE THEIR TIME STANDING IN LINE!

16

WHAT'S WRONG WITH YOU? WHY ARE YOU SITTING THERE WITH YOUR MOUTH OPEN?

YOU HAVE TO FEED ME!.. LITTLE BIRDS ARE FED BY THEIR PARENTS.

THAT'S UNTIL THEY LEARN TO FLY... THEN THEY EAT ON THEIR OWN.

WHAT?..

WHY DIDN'T YOU TELL ME THAT BEFORE? IF I'D KNOWN I'D NEVER HAVE LEARNT TO FLY!

TO HELL WITH IT!.. NOBODY EVER TELLS ME ANYTHING!

Άρκάς

©ΑΡΚΑΣ

WHAT ARE YOU DOING HERE? YOU HAVEN'T BEEN BOTHERING MY BABIES, I HOPE?..

WHAT, ME?!.. NEVER! I WAS JUST LOOKING AT THEM!

THEY'RE SO SWEET!.. AND THEY LOOK SO MUCH ALIKE! THEY'RE PRACTICALLY IDENTICAL!..

THAT'S TRUE! I OFTEN GET THEM MIXED UP MYSELF!

BUT I'VE FOUND A WAY TO TELL THEM APART!

OH YES? HOW?

THEY EACH MAKE A DIFFERENT SOUND WHEN YOU TAP THEM ON THEIR HEADS!

Apkas

©APKAS

WAAAAAAH!

WHY DOES HE KEEP CRYING? HE'S DRIVING ME INSANE!

BECAUSE HE'S HUNGRY AND HE WANTS HIS MOM!.. TAKE HIM BACK TO HER FOR FOOD!..

WAAAAAH!

I'LL FEED HIM.

WAAAAAH!

THIS WILL MAKE HIM STOP CRYING FOR SURE!

WHAT IS IT?

WAAAAH!

GLUE.

Apkas

21

HAVE YOU EVER THOUGHT ABOUT HOW BAD YOU'RE RAISING ME?.. HUH?

ALL KIDS HAVE PARENTS, A HOME, A FAMILY! AND ME, WHAT DO I HAVE?.. A FATHER WHO MY MOTHER DUMPED FOR SOMEONE ELSE!..

HOW AM I GOING TO GROW UP? WHAT ROLE MODELS DO I HAVE? HOW AM I GOING TO COPE WITH LIFE? ... DO YOU UNDERSTAND HOW TRAUMATIC ALL THIS IS FOR THE SENSITIVE SOUL OF A CHILD?..

WHY AREN'T YOU SAYING ANYTHING? ANSWER ME, HAVE YOU REALIZED WHAT ALL THIS MEANS FOR ME?

OF COURSE I HAVE!..

IT'S YOUR BATH DAY AND YOU'RE TRYING TO GET OUT OF IT.

Apkás

DARN!.. I'M TIRED OF BEING A CHILD!..

ON THE OTHER HAND, WHEN I SEE **YOU** I DON'T FEEL LIKE GROWING UP AT ALL!

WHY NOT?

DON'T YOU SEE WHY?

NO!.. EVERY AGE HAS ITS OWN ADVANTAGES.

YOU, FOR EXAMPLE, ARE CAREFREE – NO RESPONSIBILITIES, NO WORRIES...

... BUT YOU DON'T HAVE MY KNOWLEDGE AND MY BRAINS!

SURE I DON'T...

AND WHOEVER DOES SHOULD DAMN WELL GIVE THEM BACK TO YOU!

·Arkas

©ARKAS

25

TELL ME A BEDTIME STORY, DADDY.

DON'T YOU THINK IT'S TIME FOR YOU TO GO TO SLEEP WITHOUT FAIRY TALES? ...DON'T YOU THINK YOU'RE TOO OLD TO WORRY ABOUT SNOWWHITE AND LITTLE RED RIDINGHOOD?..

SO WHAT AM I SUPPOSED TO WORRY ABOUT?.. MY CHOLESTEROL?

THAT'S NOT WHAT I MEAN - STOP BEING SMART!.. I MEAN YOU SHOULD START LIVING IN REALITY AND SEE THE WORLD AS IT IS!..

... YOU'RE TOO OLD TO GO THROUGH LIFE WITH FAIRY TALES!

YES, BUT I'M TOO YOUNG TO START DRINKING!

. ApkaS

IS THAT YOUR SON?

I'M AFRAID SO!

WHY? HE'S CHARMING! HE CAME HERE AND ASKED ME TO TELL HIM A FAIRY TALE!

YES, HE LOVES FAIRY TALES...

... BUT DON'T BE FOOLED!.. HE ALSO LOVES TO SAY AND DO THE MOST REPULSIVE THINGS!

REALLY?!. AND HE SEEMS SO INNOCENT!..

THAT'S THE STRANGE THING ABOUT HIM! HE'S AN INCREDIBLE MIXTURE OF INNOCENCE AND VULGARITY!

SOMETHING LIKE LITTLE RED RIDINGHOOD IN A G-STRING!

Apkas

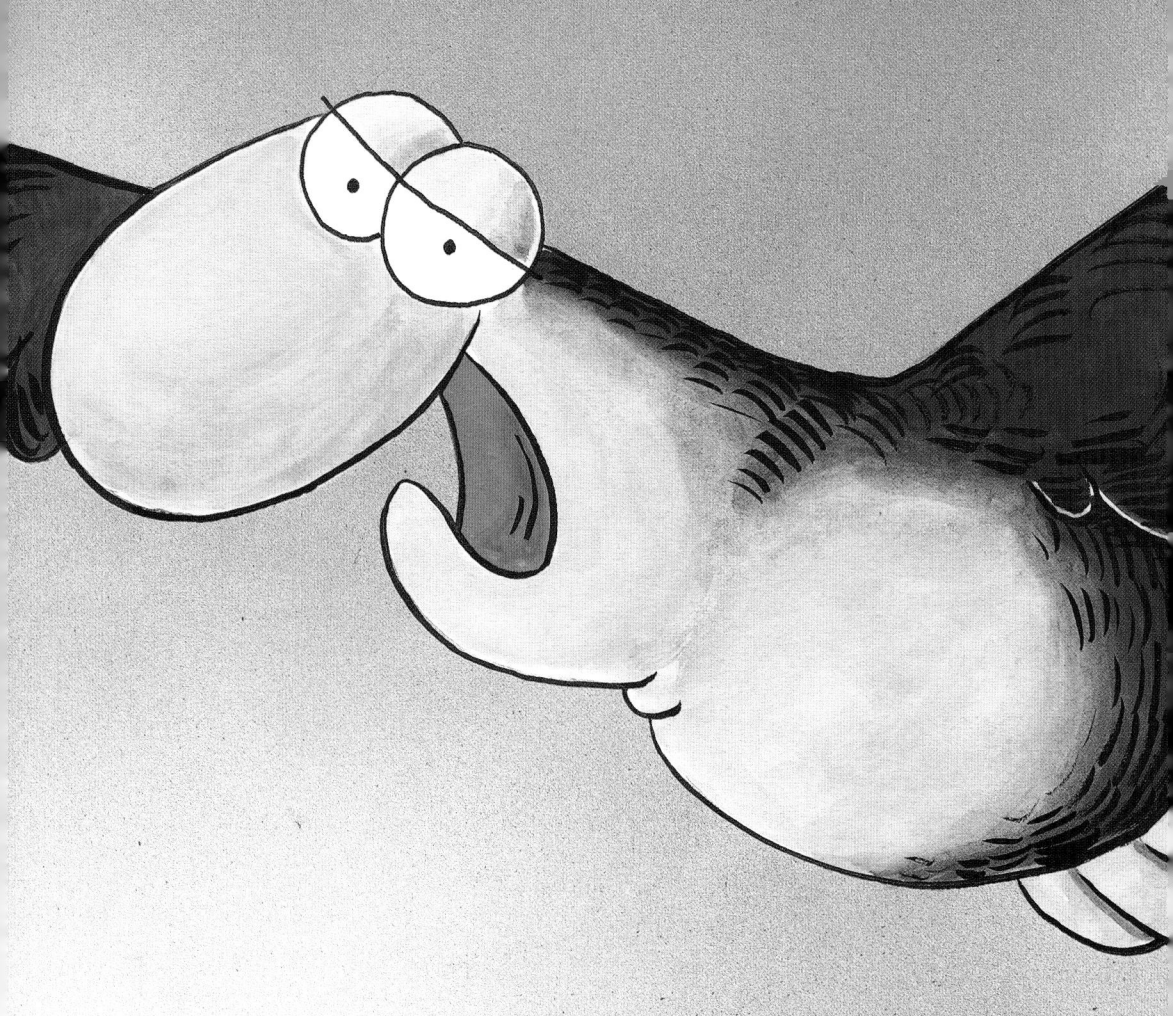

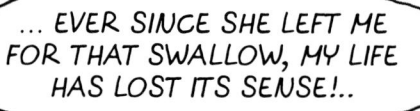

YOU CAN'T IMAGINE HOW MUCH I MISS YOUR MOTHER!..

... EVER SINCE SHE LEFT ME FOR THAT SWALLOW, MY LIFE HAS LOST ITS SENSE!..

... I THOUGHT OF SUICIDE SO OFTEN AND WITHOUT YOU I MIGHT EVEN HAVE DONE IT!..

... ONLY MY LOVE FOR YOU STILL KEEPS ME ALIVE!.. WORRYING ABOUT WHAT WILL HAPPEN TO YOU WHEN I'M DEAD!..

NEVER MIND ABOUT ME!

Aphas

I CAN'T UNDERSTAND WHY YOUR MOTHER IS STILL WITH THAT SWALLOW!.. I CAN'T UNDERSTAND WHAT SHE SEES IN HIM!.. WHAT'S HE GOT THAT I HAVEN'T?

HE'S YOUNGER THAN ME, OF COURSE... BUT THAT DOESN'T MEAN ANYTHING!..

MAYBE HE'S MORE HANDSOME THAN ME WITH HIS BEAUTIFUL BLACK FEATHERS, LARGE WINGS AND ELEGANT TAIL... BUT THAT DOESN'T MEAN ANYTHING!..

PROBABLY HE'S MORE INTELLIGENT THAN ME TOO, BECAUSE HE'S DONE A LOT OF TRAVELING AND HAS SEEN THE WORLD... BUT THAT DOESN'T MEAN ANYTHING!..

HONESTLY, I DON'T SEE WHAT HE'S GOT THAT I HAVEN'T!..

YOUR WIFE!.. BUT THAT DOESN'T MEAN ANYTHING!..

Apkäs

@APKAS

33

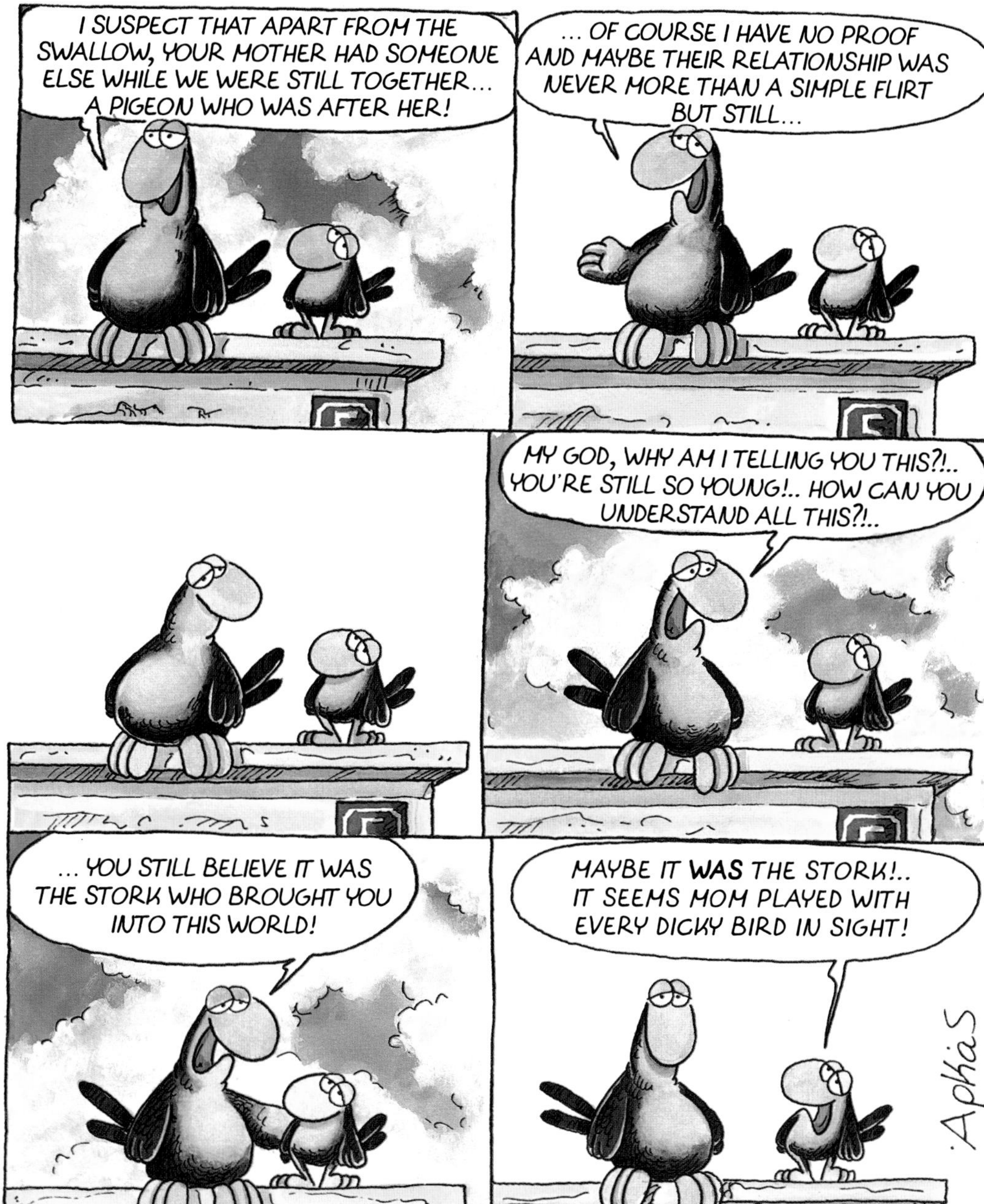

I SUSPECT THAT APART FROM THE SWALLOW, YOUR MOTHER HAD SOMEONE ELSE WHILE WE WERE STILL TOGETHER... A PIGEON WHO WAS AFTER HER!

... OF COURSE I HAVE NO PROOF AND MAYBE THEIR RELATIONSHIP WAS NEVER MORE THAN A SIMPLE FLIRT BUT STILL...

MY GOD, WHY AM I TELLING YOU THIS?!.. YOU'RE STILL SO YOUNG!.. HOW CAN YOU UNDERSTAND ALL THIS?!..

... YOU STILL BELIEVE IT WAS THE STORK WHO BROUGHT YOU INTO THIS WORLD!

MAYBE IT **WAS** THE STORK!.. IT SEEMS MOM PLAYED WITH EVERY DICKY BIRD IN SIGHT!

Apkas

35

I KNOW THAT THERE ARE LOTS OF RUMORS ABOUT MY EX-WIFE!..

I KNOW THEY SAY THAT WHILE SHE WAS WITH ME SHE WAS SEEING OTHERS ON THE SIDE!..

... BUT I DON'T BELIEVE ANY OF THAT!.. FOR ME SHE'LL ALWAYS BE THAT WONDERFUL, INNOCENT CREATURE I LOVED AND STILL LOVE WITH ALL MY HEART AND SOUL!..

... SO MUCH TIME HAS GONE BY SINCE SHE LEFT BUT I STILL MISS HER!.. EVERY MOMENT OF MY LIFE I REMEMBER HER AND I SUFFER!..

DON'T WORRY, YOU'LL GET OVER HER!..

... WE ALL GOT OVER HER!

ApkaS

OH LORD, THIS WORLD IS SO BAD AND SO IMMORAL!..

WHY, WHAT HAS IT DONE TO YOU?

WHEREVER I GO, WHOEVER I SPEAK TO, I'M FOREVER HEARING DIRTY HINTS ABOUT YOUR MOTHER!.. THEY KEEP INSINUATING THAT SHE WAS UNFAITHFUL TO ME AND THAT SHE DATED ALL SORTS OF OTHER BIRDS!..

... IF YOU LISTEN TO THEM YOU'D THINK THAT SHE HAD BEEN WITH EVERYONE ELSE EXCEPT FOR ME!

LET THEM TALK!.. YOU'VE STILL GOT ME TO LOVE YOU!

WHAT GOOD IS THAT? YOU DON'T EVEN TREAT ME WELL!

WHAT?! ME, I DON'T TREAT YOU WELL?!.

... WHEN I TREAT YOU LIKE YOU'RE MY FATHER?!.

Apkas

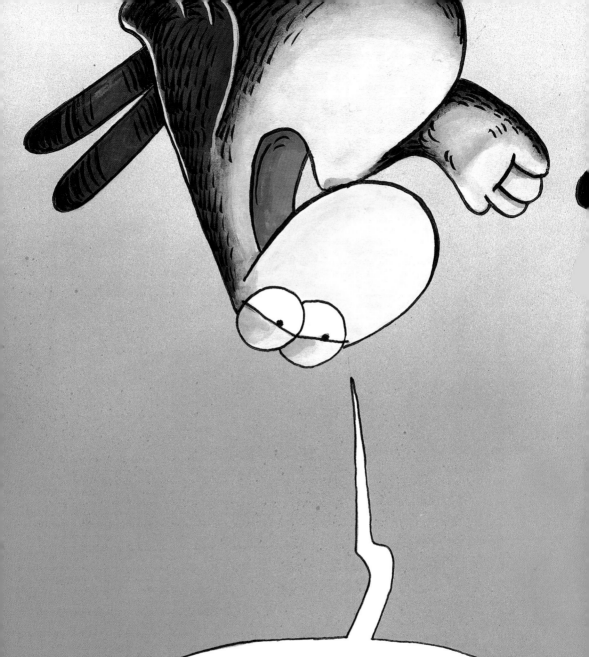

41

OH MY GOD! MY HUSBAND! WHAT'S HAPPENED?

HE'S NOT TOO WELL!.. HE'S DEAD!

OH, NO!.. NO!.. HIS HEART! I KNEW THIS WOULD HAPPEN ONE DAY!

BE BRAVE, MADAM!

PLEASE TELL ME, DID HE SAY ANYTHING BEFORE HE DIED?.. DID HE MENTION ME?

UH... YEAH... SURE...

... HE SAID THAT HE LOVED YOU AND... THAT HE WAS VERY HAPPY WITH YOU!..

REALLY?

ABSOLUTELY! HE SWORE ON HIS LIFE!

Apkas

WHEN I SAW THAT POOR WOMAN WEEPING AND MOURNING I THOUGHT OF YOUR MOTHER...

... I WONDERED HOW YOUR MOTHER WOULD REACT IF SHE HEARD THAT I HAD DIED... WHAT WOULD SHE DO IF SOMEONE WENT AND TOLD HER THAT I WAS DEAD?

SHE'D BE A WRECK.

DO YOU THINK SO?..

SURE!.. WRACKING HER BRAINS TRYING TO REMEMBER WHO YOU WERE.

Apha.S

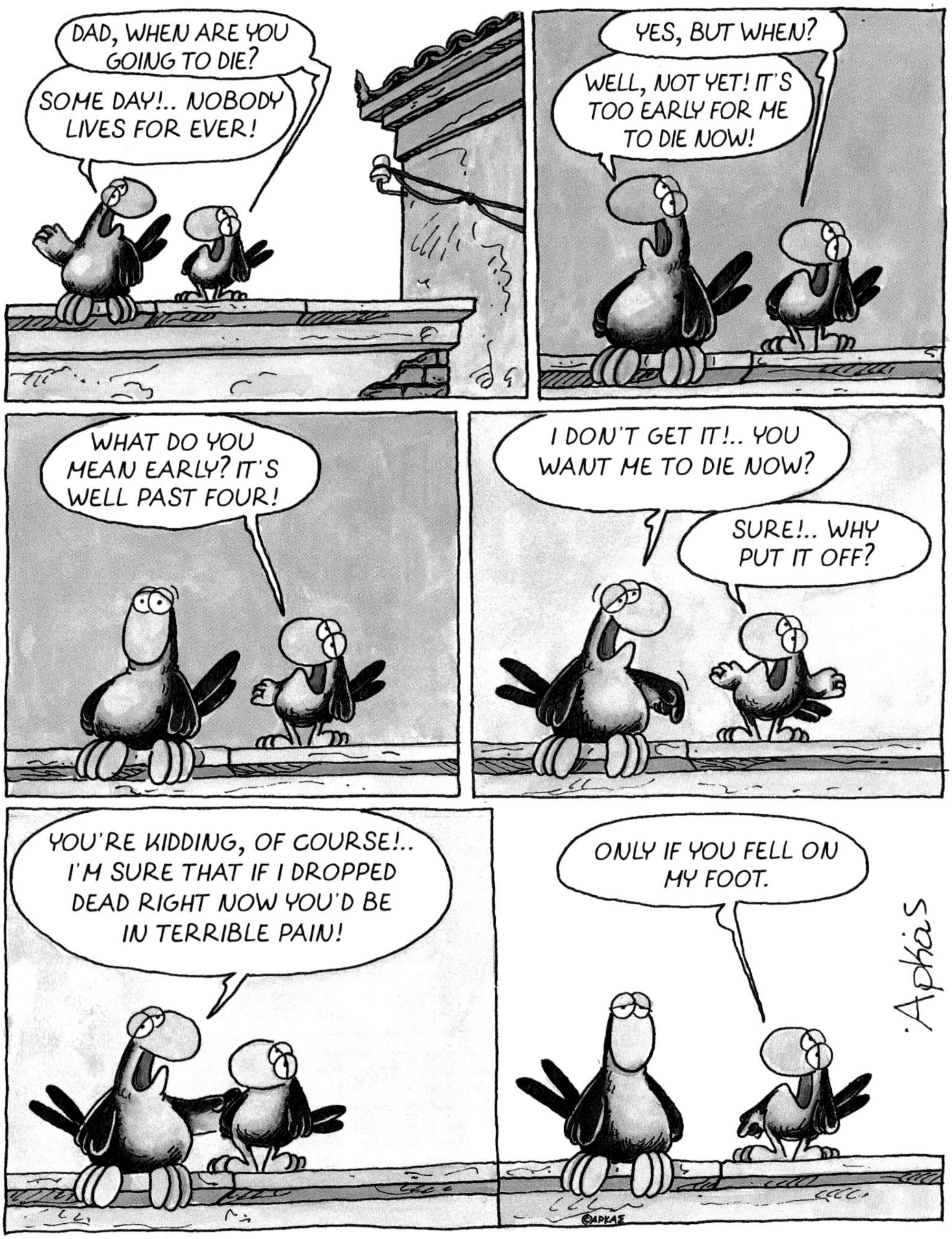

44

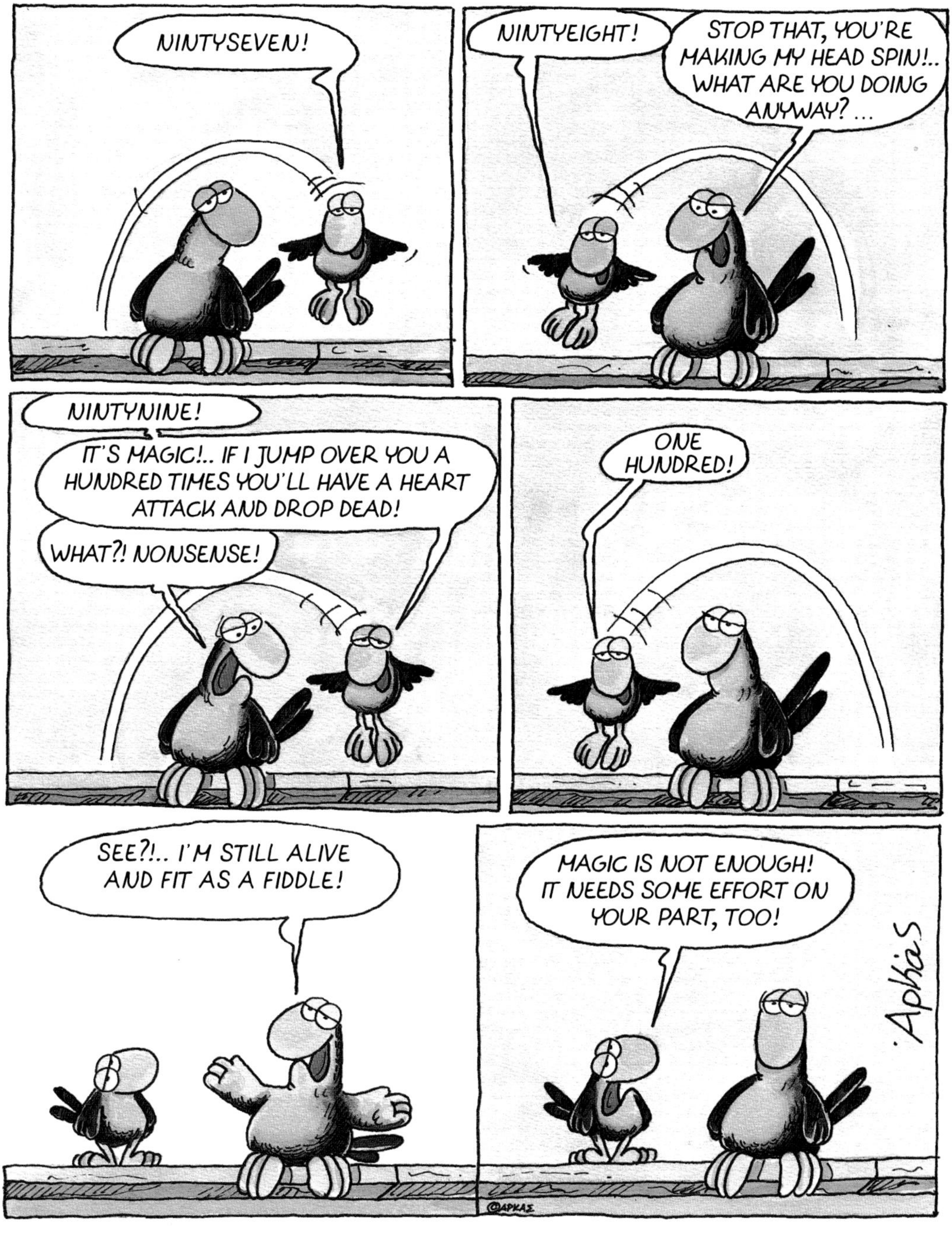

NINTYSEVEN!

NINTYEIGHT!

STOP THAT, YOU'RE MAKING MY HEAD SPIN!.. WHAT ARE YOU DOING ANYWAY? ...

NINTYNINE!

IT'S MAGIC!.. IF I JUMP OVER YOU A HUNDRED TIMES YOU'LL HAVE A HEART ATTACK AND DROP DEAD!

WHAT?! NONSENSE!

ONE HUNDRED!

SEE?!.. I'M STILL ALIVE AND FIT AS A FIDDLE!

MAGIC IS NOT ENOUGH! IT NEEDS SOME EFFORT ON YOUR PART, TOO!

Apkas

TELL ME, DAD, WHEN EXACTLY DID MOM GO OFF WITH THAT SWALLOW?

I TOLD YOU, JUST AFTER YOU WERE BORN.

SO IF I'D BEEN BORN A LITTLE LATER, THE SWALLOW MIGHT HAVE BEEN MY FATHER, RIGHT?

MAYBE...

DAMN IT! WHY DID I HAVE TO HURRY?!

WONDERFUL! ... MY WIFE LEFT ME FOR SOMEONE ELSE AND MY SON DOESN'T WANT ME AS A FATHER!..

WHY?.. WHERE DID I GO WRONG?.. IS IT MY FAULT?.. WHY ALL THESE FAMILY PROBLEMS?

WHAT FAMILY PROBLEMS?..

... TO HAVE FAMILY PROBLEMS YOU FIRST NEED TO HAVE A FAMILY!

Apkas

ΟΔΟΣ ΟΡΝΙΘΩΝ
ORNITHON ST.

52

I CAN SEE YOU DON'T LIKE ME BUT I DON'T KNOW WHY NOT.

TELL ME, WHAT'S THE MATTER? WHAT'S THE PROBLEM? WHERE DID I GO WRONG?

HERE I AM, ALL ALONE - NO WIFE, NO FRIENDS, NO NOTHING! ALL FOR YOUR SAKE!..

EVER SINCE YOUR MOTHER LEFT I'VE GIVEN UP EVERYTHING IN ORDER TO BE FATHER AND MOTHER TO YOU!..

... TELL ME, WHAT ELSE CAN I DO?

YOU'D BETTER BE THE CHILD AS WELL, BECAUSE ANY MINUTE NOW I'LL BE LEAVING, TOO!

Arkas

©ΑΡΚΑΣ

EXCUSE ME, SIR, DO YOU KNOW THE WAY TO AFRICA?

AFRICA?.. WHY DO YOU WANT TO GO THERE?

I WANT TO FIND MY MOM! MY MOM LEFT ME AND MY DAD AND WENT SOUTH! NOW I'M LEAVING MY DAD TO GO AND FIND MY MOM.

AND YOUR DAD?

MY DAD HAS NO-ONE TO LEAVE, SO HE'S STAYING HERE!

OKAY, BUT HOW CAN YOU BE SURE YOU'LL FIND YOUR MOM IN AFRICA?

THAT'S NOT SO IMPORTANT!.. WHAT'S IMPORTANT TO ME IS TO LEAVE MY DAD!

THEN WHY DON'T YOU GO SOMEWHERE NEAR HERE?.. DO YOU HAVE TO GO ON SUCH A DANGEROUS LONG JOURNEY TO LEAVE HIM?

THAT'S THE WAY I AM!..

... WHEN IT COMES TO MY FATHER, I SPARE NEITHER TOIL NOR TROUBLE!

Apkas

@APKAZ

EXCUSE ME, SIR, HAVE YOU SEEN A LITTLE SPARROW ANYWHERE?

YES... BUT WHY ARE YOU SO UPSET?

I'M HIS FATHER!

OH, I SEE!.. IN THAT CASE YOU'RE AWFULLY CALM...

YOUR SON WAS HERE A LITTLE WHILE AGO AND TOLD ME HE WAS GOING SOUTH TO FIND HIS MOTHER.

OH MY GOD!.. HE REALLY DID IT!.. I'LL GO OUT OF MY MIND!...

IF I WERE YOU I WOULDN'T WORRY TOO MUCH!.. IT'S IMPOSSIBLE FOR HIM TO TRAVEL THAT FAR ON HIS OWN! HE'LL FLY FOR A WHILE AND WHEN HE GETS TIRED HE'LL COME BACK HOME!

YOU DON'T KNOW HIM! YOU HAVE NO IDEA HOW PIGHEADED HE IS!

SOUTH

·Aphás

54

WE'LL STOP HERE FOR A REST!

WHY? I'M NOT TIRED AT ALL.

BUT I AM!.. GET OFF, I'M LEAVING YOU HERE!

YOU'RE LEAVING ME?!

SURELY YOU'RE JOKING!.. YOU CAN'T LEAVE ME HERE IN THE MIDDLE OF NOWHERE!

I'M SORRY, MY BOY, BUT I CAN'T CARRY YOU ANY MORE!.. YOU'LL HAVE TO GET BY ON YOUR OWN!..

ARE YOU KIDDING?! I GREW UP IN A CITY!.. HOW CAN I POSSIBLY GET BY ON MY OWN, AMONGST ALL THESE PLANTS AND BUSHES?.. WHO DO YOU THINK I AM? MOWGLI?..

...WHAT CAN I DO HERE? HOW SHALL I LIVE? WHAT SHALL I EAT?

LOOK DOWN... THE GROUND IS FULL OF SEEDS!

OH NO!.. SO I'LL EVEN HAVE TO SWEEP?!

Αρκάς

ALL THE BIRDS OF THE AIR FELL A-SIGHING AND A-SOBBING ♪♫

HERE WE ARE! I'M LOST NOW THAT THAT STUPID STORK DUMPED ME!..

... NOW WHAT SHALL I DO, A POOR LITTLE CHILD, LOST AND ALL ALONE IN THE WOODS?

GOOD LORD!.. LUCKY I'M NOT A GIRL, OTHERWISE THE BIG BAD WOLF COULD COME BY AND TAKE ME FOR LITTLE RED RIDINGHOOD!..

... OR THE WICKED WITCH COULD COME BY AND TAKE ME FOR SNOWWHITE!..

... OR, EVEN WORSE, THE SEVEN DWARFS COULD COME BY AND TAKE ME ONE AFTER THE OTHER!

GOOD AFTERNOON!.. COULD YOU HELP ME, SIR? ... I'M LOST IN THE WOODS.

YOU'RE LOST?.. HA!.. YOU MUST BE VERY STUPID, KID!.. BIRDS DON'T EVER GET LOST IN THE WOODS.

I GOT LOST BECAUSE I'M A CITY BIRD!.. I'M NOT A COUNTRY BUMPKIN!

WHAT! SO I'M A BUMPKIN?

MAYBE YOU WANT ME TO GO AWAY?.. HUH?... MAYBE IT'S BENEATH YOUR DIGNITY TO SIT WITH A BUMPKIN?..

... OR MAYBE I SMELL?!.. MAYBE YOU'RE DISTURBED BY MY SMELL?... ARE YOU?

ARE YOU THROUGH? ...'COS I CAN'T HOLD MY BREATH ANY LONGER.

Arkás

@ΑΡΚΑΣ

I'M OFF, GOOD-BYE!

WHAT'S THAT? SOME JERK LEFT HIS CHEWING GUM ON THIS TREE!

OH DEAR! THAT'S BIRDLIME!

YOU SAT DOWN ON LIME, KID, AND NOW YOU'RE STUCK AND CAN'T GET AWAY!

YOU DIDN'T HAVE TO DO THAT!.. YOU ONLY HAD TO ASK ME POLITELY AND I'D HAVE STAYED.

YOU DON'T UNDERSTAND!.. IT'S A TRAP!.. THEY USE BIRDLIME TO CATCH SONGBIRDS OR BIRDS WITH PRETTY FEATHERS AND THEN PUT THEM INTO CAGES AND SELL THEM!..

GOOD LORD! SO NOW THEY'RE GOING TO PUT ME IN A CAGE?

DON'T WORRY!.. YOU'RE A SPARROW! ...YOU DON'T HAVE A BEAUTIFUL VOICE OR GOOD LOOKS, SO THEY'LL LET YOU GO!

OH REALLY?..

... BUT WHAT IF THEY DISCOVER MY WONDERFUL HIDDEN QUALITIES?

Apkàs

©APKAI

DAD!..

MY SON!.. YOU'RE BACK!

ARE YOU ALRIGHT?.. I WAS WORRIED TO DEATH!.. I WAS TOLD YOU WERE SEEN GOING SOUTH ON A STORK AND I THOUGHT IT WAS A CASE OF KIDNAPPING!

OH NO, NOT KIDNAPPING!.. HE CAME OF HIS OWN FREE WILL!..

...BUT THEN HE CHANGED HIS MIND, STUPID STORK, AND HE DUMPED ME IN A FOREST WHERE I GOT LOST AND IN THE END I GOT TRAPPED ON BIRDLIME!.. BUT THEN THE TRAPPERS CAME AND SET ME FREE BECAUSE I DIDN'T HAVE A BEAUTIFUL VOICE OR PRETTY FEATHERS!..

...AND THEN I WAS UNHAPPY BECAUSE I FELT UNWANTED, 'COS THE STORK ABANDONED ME AND THE TRAPPERS DIDN'T WANT ME EITHER, NOT EVEN TO PUT ME IN A CAGE, AND THEN I FELT VERY SAD AND LONELY!..

...AND THEN I REMEMBERED THAT THERE IS ONE PERSON IN THIS WORLD WHO LOVES ME VERY MUCH AND WHO I ADORE AND CAN'T SEE ENOUGH OF BECAUSE I FEEL GOOD ONLY WHEN I SEE HIM! AND SO I CAME BACK...

DEAR SON!

...TO GET MY MIRROR.

Apkas

©APKAΣ

59

I'VE MADE UP MY MIND, DAD! I'M NEVER GOING TO LEAVE THE CITY AGAIN!.. I DIDN'T LIKE IT AT ALL IN THE COUNTRY!

WHY NOT?

BECAUSE THEY'VE RUINED THE ENVIRONMENT! THEY'VE PULLED DOWN ALL THE HOUSES, THEY'VE GOT RID OF ALL THE CARS AND THEY'VE PUT DIRT EVERYWHERE AND THEY'VE COVERED UP THE ASPHALT!.. BUT EVEN IF THERE WAS ANY ASPHALT THE CARS WOULDN'T BE ABLE TO PASS ANYWAY BECAUSE THE PLACE IS FULL OF TREES!..

...ONLY A FEW TELEPHONE POLES ARE LEFT BUT I EXPECT THEY'LL CHOP THEM DOWN SOON AND REPLACE THEM WITH TREES!.. IT'S INCREDIBLE, THIS OBSESSION WITH DESTROYING NATURE IN ORDER TO MAKE TREES!..

... JUST THINK, THEY HAVEN'T EVEN LEFT A SINGLE TELEVISION AERIAL FOR THE BIRDS TO SIT ON, SO THEY ALL HAVE TO PERCH ON TREES INSTEAD!

YOU'VE GOT IT ALL WRONG, KID!..

...TREES ARE NATURE!.. AND WE BIRDS WERE NOT MADE TO SIT ON TELEVISION AERIALS... OUR NATURAL PLACE IS IN THE TREES!

THAT'S A GOOD ONE!

...IF THAT WERE TRUE, WISE GUY, WE WOULDN'T HAVE FEET, WE'D HAVE STALKS!

Άρκάς

©ΑΡΚΑΣ

SO YOU'VE DECIDED YOU DON'T LIKE TRAVELING?

I LIKE IT A LOT, AS LONG AS IT'S PEOPLE WHO ANNOY ME WHO ARE DOING THE TRAVELING!

YOU, FOR EXAMPLE, WHEN ARE YOU GOING TO TRAVEL?

WHERE SHOULD I TRAVEL TO?

YOU COULD GO SOUTH, WHERE MOM IS... AFTER ALL YOU'RE THE ONLY ONE WHO CAN MAKE HER COME BACK.

NO POINT! YOUR MOTHER WILL NEVER BE PERSUADED TO COME BACK TO ME!

I DIDN'T MEAN THAT SHE SHOULD COME BACK TO YOU! I MEANT THAT YOU SHOULD STAY THERE, SO THAT SHE'LL HAVE TO COME BACK HERE TO AVOID SEEING YOU!

AHA!.. YOUR MOTHER DOESN'T WANT ME THERE AND YOU DON'T WANT ME HERE... I'LL HAVE TO FACE THE FACT THAT I'M UNWANTED EVERYWHERE!

NOW LET'S NOT EXAGGERATE! NOT EVERYWHERE!..

ONLY ON THIS PLANET!

ApkaS

©ΑΡΚΑΣ

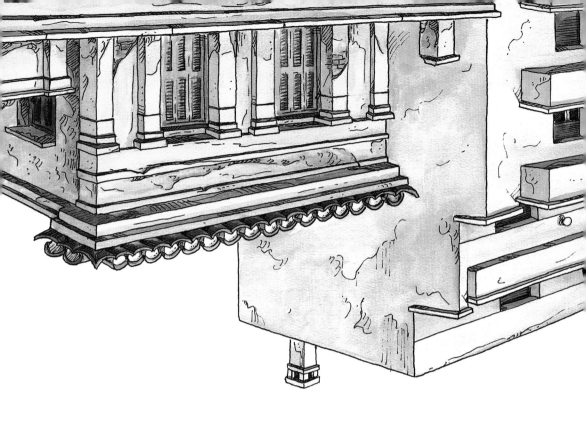

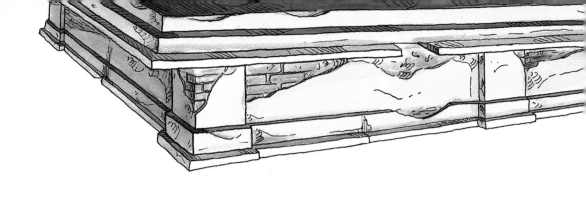